THE DRUMMER BOY
THE BOY WITH THE BALL

Author
Charity Simmons

Illustrator
Meredith Locke

Copyright 2020, 2021
Published by PsAbide91

A young boy, gifted with raw talent on the drums and on the basketball court faces an unseen obstacle. Will he overcome it? Will fear set in and prevent him from reaching his full potential? Based on real life events, this poetic story encompasses a boy's journey through an emotional feat that seemed impossible to overcome. With support and strategies to process an emotional storm, anyone can overcome and find their voice, strength and power to weather the storm and reach their destiny.

Caregiver's Guide to Taking Every Thought Captive

We have all experienced a bad dream, nightmare and maybe even a cyclical pattern of thoughts that are worrisome, unsettling and have a potentially negative impact on emotions, sleep patterns or daily tasks.

When my son MJ began experiencing some nightmares and negative thoughts that made him afraid, disrupted his sleep, and began to impact his desire to do the things he loves, like playing the drums and basketball, I knew we had to dig into those thoughts and support him to manage his emotions and overcome them. As a family of faith, we look to the Word of God which is our foundation for overcoming, managing our emotions. As a school counselor, I have few strategies from my professional toolkit as well. This story brings them both together!

As parents we try to shield our children and manage what they are exposed to, but in this world today, the ease of access to all content in media and technology seems to lack boundaries and it's almost impossible to keep your child from being exposed to certain things. Nevertheless, we should still try!

Through life experience and as a school counselor supporting many students and their parents process and work through a variety of situations, I do believe that we receive ideas and thoughts through our five senses, the lenses to our mind. What we see, hear, taste, touch and smell can insight curiosities and ideas, create space for fear, trigger memories and previous trauma of others or one's own. Even some things viewed on the news, or even just heard or spoken in conversation can get the mind thinking. So how do we process or help our children process all the information that comes through the lenses of their senses?

Mrs. Simmons' Sentiments:

1. Conversation Check Ins with your child.
Talk with your child regularly in conversation about what they are thinking and feeling. Dig deeper into the thoughts and feelings as your child is comfortable opening up. If your child is experiencing nightmares or negative thoughts, try to find the root cause. What is it about? What is happening? When does it occur?

2. Interrupt the Thought Pattern.
Be intentional about changing the subject. The mind cannot dwell on two things at once. How can you interrupt a thought pattern or cycle? Pray. Sing a favorite song. Change the scenery. Read a book. Play a game. Engage in Physical Activity. Get outside if during the day. Empower their voice. Empower them with the truth.

3. Process the thought dream or nightmare during the day when emotions are normal and regulated, but not near the next nap or bedtime. Ask what was it about? Is that real or fake? Could this really happen or not? Discuss what is safe, true, and real?

4. Implement a Plan for what to do when the thought or nightmare occurs. Choose a person the child can come to when the thought/dream occurs. Choose two options to interrupt the cyclical pattern that the child can remember to do. Reiterate what is safe, true and real?

For more information on processing your own thoughts and helping your children do the same, visit psabide91.org or use the qr code.

Dedicated to my son, Marcus Jr.
May you continue to use your voice and
be empowered by the Holy Spirit to take
every thought captive!

PsAbide91

STAY. REMAIN. DWELL.

He woke to the
beat of the drums
in his head. Early
in the morning,
he got out of bed.

MJ tiptoed through the hall to see if anyone was up. Not yet. Just him, the young, eager bruch.

The beat became much clearer as he rubbed his sweet brown eyes. He could feel it in his heart, it was time to arise.

So he walked to his room, put on his headphones and drummed the beat.
The praise rising up

THUD,

cling,

clang,

REPEAT

Just a boy with his tattered, tan drumsticks with a praise and a call from the Lord.

After breakfast, he washed up and dressed himself from head to toe. The shirt, shorts, and socks had to match as if he had some place to go.

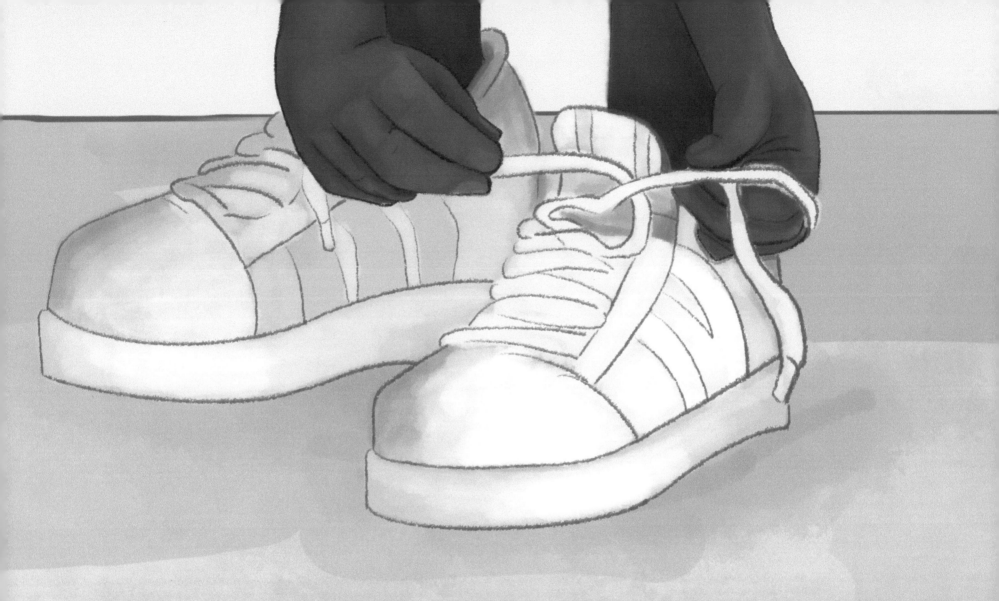

He laced his shoes and tied them, as best as he could, with two bows.

Then he dribbled his favorite ball to the backyard to practice free throws.

He dribbled, he crossed, he spun, shot, and scored. He made lots of goals! The drive within, the talent given, was purposed by the Lord. Just a boy with joy, his basketball, and a call from the Lord.

In the stillness of the afternoon something changed all of a sudden. The drummer boy, the boy with the ball, came crying to his mother. He was speechless and sobbing, tears rolling down his face.

What is going on?
What happened? His
mother's heart raced.

She wrapped her arms around him. She squeezed and hugged him tight. She said, "Son, take a deep breath, everything is going to be alright. Let's calm down and breathe so we can talk about it. Deep breath in through your nose and out through your mouth, slowly, that's it. You've got it".

He said, "I was in my room resting on my bed and scary thoughts came into my head".

"Oh Mj, what thoughts did you have this time? Let's talk about it. Are these thoughts something that is good and true? Are these thoughts coming from you?"

You see the drummer boy, the boy with the ball, plays the drums for the Lord and honors God on the court. The drive within is not just him, but something more the evil one wants to destroy. As he talked with his mother about the scary thoughts, she said, "Remember whose you are. If the thought does not match who God says you are, BEWARE! It's a trap! Don't let it go too far!"

When scary thoughts come into your mind, shout NO!" And call upon the Lord. Remember he will never leave you nor forsake you. His angels are encamped all around you, protecting you from harm.

MJ thought about the words his mother said. "What did God promise? He will never leave me or forsake me. So I know I am not alone."

His mother reminded him, not every thought that comes into your mind is yours. Test it and see before you accept it as your own. MJ said to his mother the question she asks him when scary thoughts come to his mind. "Hmmm, I'll test it and see. Is it pure, just, and of a good report from the One living inside of me?"

Not every thought that comes into your mind is yours.
Test it and see! Is it what the Bible tells me about me?
Does it encourage, build up, or affirm me?
Or does it lie, hurt or seek to destroy me?
Test it and see!
Test it and see!

So the drummer boy, the boy with the ball, put the evil one in his place. Under his feet, not in his head and continued to walk by faith. He prayed this prayer with his mom that day and every night before bed. When he prayed this prayer, the evil one's thoughts could no longer stay in his head.

I am a child of God.
I am son of the King.
I am chosen, I am not alone!
I am loved, God calls me His own.
He is with me, so I will not fear.
Father God, please hold me near.
I have peace in Jesus' name.
No worries, no more fears!
I have confidence when I call His name.
In Him I can do all things, through
Christ the Lord who strengthens me!

When the evil one tried to put thoughts in his head, he overcame them by the power of the Lord. He used his voice to speak God's Word. God's Word is the almighty force!

When we speak the Word, the evil one has to flee. He cannot abide where God's presence is, and God's presence lives in me!

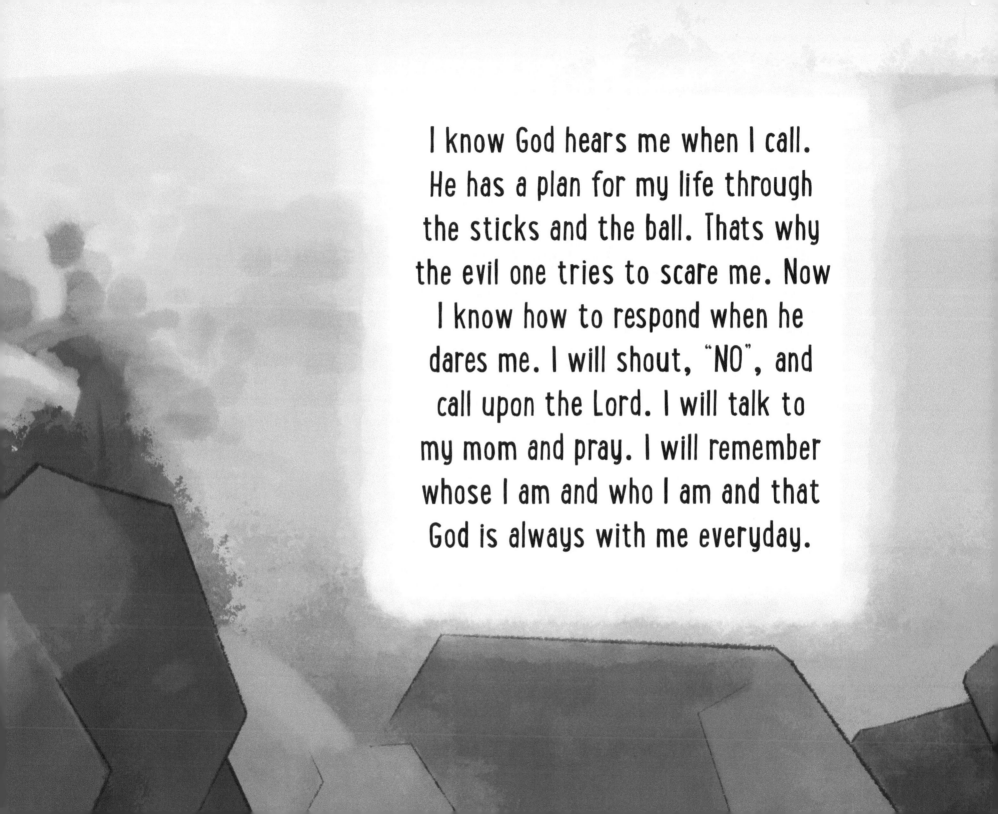

I know God hears me when I call.
He has a plan for my life through
the sticks and the ball. Thats why
the evil one tries to scare me. Now
I know how to respond when he
dares me. I will shout, "NO", and
call upon the Lord. I will talk to
my mom and pray. I will remember
whose I am and who I am and that
God is always with me everyday.

Finally, brethren, whatever things are true, whatever things are noble, whatever things are just, whatever things are pure, whatever things are lovely, whatever things are of good report, if there is any virtue and if there is anything praiseworthy - meditate (think) on these things.

Philippians 4:8

We demolish arguments and every pretension that sets itself up against the knowledge of God and we take captive every thought to make it obedient to Christ.

2 Corinthians 10:5

CPSIA information can be obtained
at www.ICGtesting.com
Printed in the USA
BVHW061536080721
611451BV00004B/105

* 9 7 8 0 5 7 8 9 3 4 7 2 3 *